For Rita
Somewhere over the rainbow

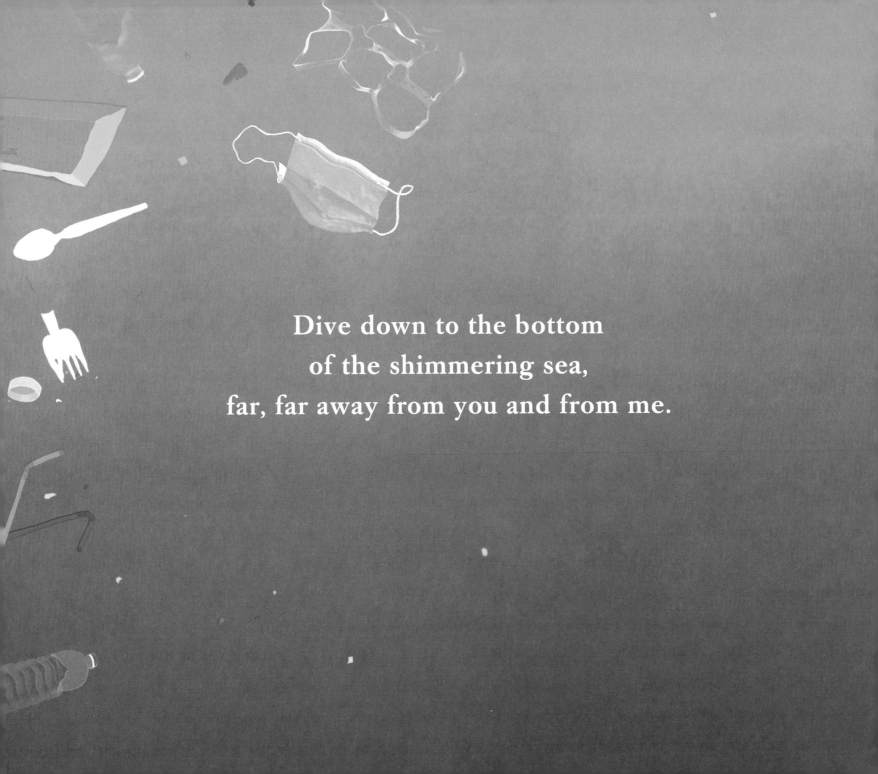

Dive down to the bottom
of the shimmering sea,
far, far away from you and from me.

For this is where you'll find
Jessie the jellyfish,
bobbing through tonnes of rotting rubbish.

"Where are the fish?"
I hear you ask.

You used to see them with
a snorkel and mask.

The sea was once ever so clean.
Now there's only the odd sardine.

Jessie searched all around
but her friends were nowhere to be found.

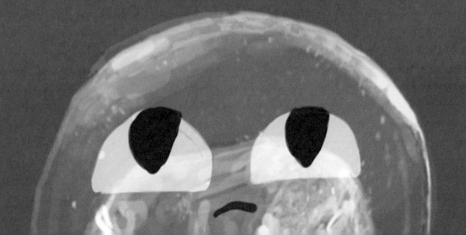

"Are you one of my friends?" she cried, to a bag left drifting with the tide.

Its tentacles were far
too stubby,

and it found
nothing very funny.

But Jessie longed
to find a friend,

so maybe she would
just pretend...

Where had the
other sea folk gone?

Had they packed up
and all moved on?

At Mermaid Corner,
the mermaids
weren't home.

They no longer
danced in the fun
frothy foam.

Jessie thought they
were all alone,

when **suddenly**
she heard a groan.

"Oh Jessie, you gave me such a fright!
There isn't a Dover sole in sight.

The sea is now a giant bin.
Even my home is a baked bean tin."

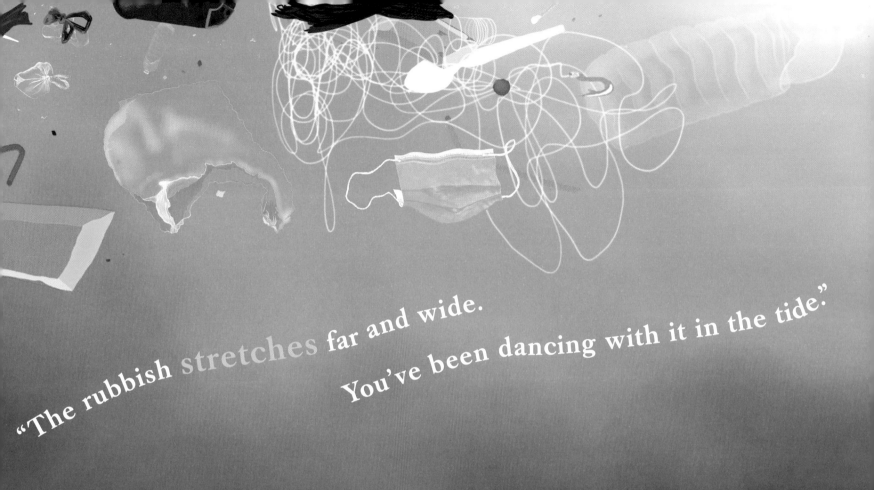

"The rubbish stretches far and wide.
You've been dancing with it in the tide."

"Even your new 'friend' over there
was dropped with very little care."

Then suddenly with a
splish and a **splash**,
the Hoomans began to pick
up their trash!

The bendy straws,
the spiky forks,
even the bags
and bottle corks.

With the coral
sparkling
super bright, and hardly
any litter in sight.

They could
tumble, turn
and **twist** through
the night.

The mermaids were finally back on the rocks,

combing and plaiting their long, luscious locks.

Even the rays from nearby Ray Bay,
returned to **party, have fun** and **play!**

So, **pick up** your straws and dinner forks,
the plastic bags and bottle corks.

We'll be one step closer to a **cleaner** sea,
and the beach a nicer place to be.

+

INCLUDES
12 HOURS
OF LESSON
PLANS

Lesson plans that meet national
curriculum guidelines have also been written
for Jessie The Jellyfish by Arts2Educate.

If you are a teacher and you need resources to
use alongside teaching then please
get in touch.

info@jessiejellyfish.co.uk